BOOK OF SECRETS

W9-BSR-656

Property of:

JULIEN♡ poopy

ABOUT YOU

I love doing . . .

Praying to God

I hate doing . . .

Saying bad words / Punching

My favorite ninja is . . .

Fire

My favorite movie is . . .

Pokemon

My favorite song is . . .

My favorite book is . . .

I would describe myself in these three words:

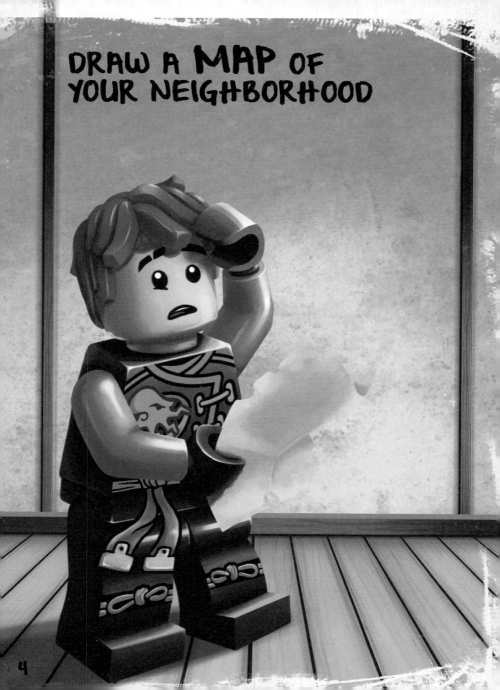

DRAW A **MAP** OF YOUR NEIGHBORHOOD

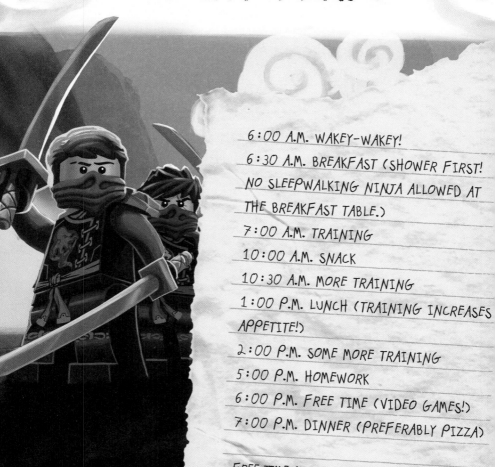

A DAY IN THE LIFE OF THE
NINJA TEAM

6:00 A.M. WAKEY-WAKEY!

6:30 A.M. BREAKFAST (SHOWER FIRST! NO SLEEPWALKING NINJA ALLOWED AT THE BREAKFAST TABLE.)

7:00 A.M. TRAINING

10:00 A.M. SNACK

10:30 A.M. MORE TRAINING

1:00 P.M. LUNCH (TRAINING INCREASES APPETITE!)

2:00 P.M. SOME MORE TRAINING

5:00 P.M. HOMEWORK

6:00 P.M. FREE TIME (VIDEO GAMES!)

7:00 P.M. DINNER (PREFERABLY PIZZA)

FREE TIME (MORE VIDEO GAMES—FOR THOSE WHO HAVEN'T FALLEN ASLEEP ALREADY)

WHAT IS YOUR DAILY DRILL?

1.

2.

3.

4.

5.

6.

7.

8.

9.

10.

YOU OWN A RESTAURANT FOR NINJA!
What's on the menu?

Breakfast:

Lunch:

Dinner:

Dessert: Finally!!!

Something to drink, maybe?

THINGS A **NINJA** SHOULD KNOW:

what do you think a **ninja** should know?

NINJA SPOTLIGHT

Describe yourself as a famous **ninja**.

What would you say to your fans?

What would you be famous for?

BE LIKE **MASTER WU**

You become Master Wu for a day.
What would **YOU** do?

YOU'VE FOUND PIRATE TREASURE!

What do you do first?

1. I run away from the pirates.

2.

3.

4.

5.

6.

7.

8.

THE WORST DAY EVER

Write about a crazy day you've had.
What happened?

What would have made your day awesome instead?

YOU'VE FOUND A
MAGIC LAMP!

what are your three wishes?

FIRST WISH:

SECOND WISH:

THIRD WISH:

Watch out!
The djinn could
trap you!

DISGUISE THE NINJA!
CAN YOU MAKE THEM UNRECOGNIZABLE?

Design your own
wanted poster

DISGUSTING PIZZA!

Imagine the grossest pizza possible!

INGREDIENTS:

DESIGN YOUR OWN FLAG
It can even be a pirate flag!

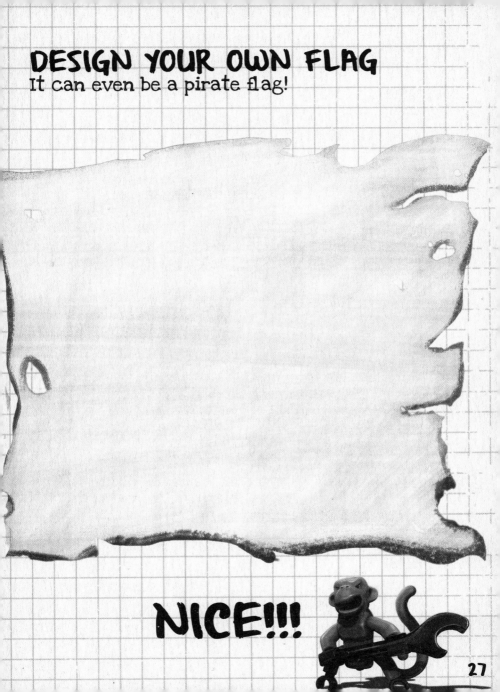

NICE!!!

How do you feel? Are you different? What do you do for fun?

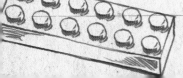

WRITE YOUR OWN COMIC

TITLE

THE SKY PIRATES HAVE BEEN PREYING ON SEASIDE TOWNS IN THEIR RAID ZEPPELIN.

ZANE IS CLOSING IN BUT . . .

NINJA ALWAYS
LOOK COOL

Design a cool **ninja outfit** you'd like to wear.

There's nothing like a good team!

Draw your dream team and describe their powers.

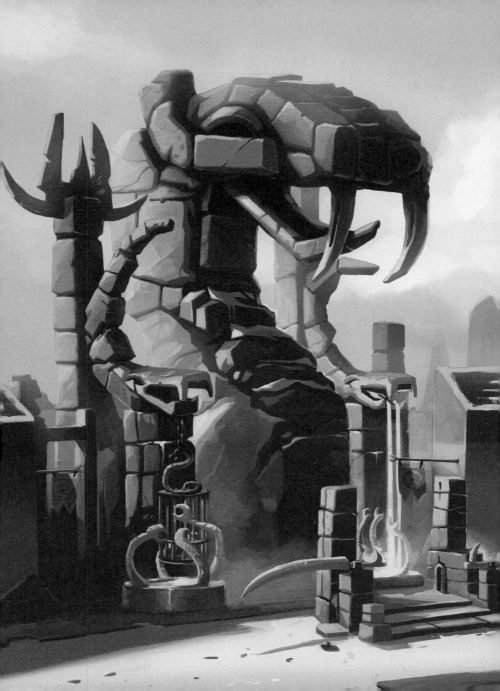

WHAT ARE THE BEST ADVENTURES YOU'VE EVER HAD?

FIRST:

SECOND:

THIRD:

HOW WOULD YOU
SURVIVE IN THE WILD?

Here's what Jay would take with him:

1. The book *How to Survive in the Wild*

2. A TV (Can't live without it!)

3. A Sofa

4. The whole house, just in case the sofa gets damaged in the open air

5. A few best friends

6. Two big sacks of snacks and a store full of video games

7. A training dojo, of course!

What would you take with you?

1.

2.

3.

4.

5.

6.

Who likes building more than **CLEANING?**

List ten of your favorite things to build with LEGO® bricks:

1.

2.

3.

4.

5.

6.

7.

8.

9.

10.

FRIENDS CARICATURE
HALL OF FAME

Draw your friends and family members as ninja.

WHO IS
THIS?

FRIENDS CARICATURE
HALL OF FAME

PETS INCLUDED!

HA HA :)
FUNNY!

IF YOU WERE A NINJA WITH THE POWER TO TRAVEL THROUGH TIME:

You would travel to . . .

You would meet . . .

You would wear . . .

Forward:

_____
_____
_____
_____
_____

Slow-Mo:

_____
_____
_____
_____
_____

Pause:

_____
_____
_____
_____
_____

Reversal:

_____
_____
_____
_____
_____

Finish the story, young ninja. Perhaps it will be passed from ninja to ninja for many years to come.

The night was so dark that the ninja could barely see his own hands. He'd already bumped twice into a tree and fallen into a puddle, but he still moved on. He had to finish his mission. To his relief he saw a small light ahead. It was Master Wu showing him the way. At least the ninja knew which direction to go.
Suddenly he heard a loud rustle along the path and a dark shadow jumped out of the bushes . . .

THE TALE OF THE DARK SHADOW

DRAW A PANORAMA OF YOUR HOMETOWN

BEWARE OF GHOOOOSTS!

Draw a ghost that would **scare** even Master Wu!

IT'S YOUR BIRTHDAY!

Design the party decorations and a ninja-themed **birthday cake**.

If you had your own tea shop, where would you get new flavors? What skills would you like your tea to enhance?

- For example, extract of dried carrot, nettle leaves and juicy jelly beans could help your observation skills.

The tea I make with rose petals and oak bark gives me strength, energy, and keeps my mind fresh.

WHAT SHOULD A REAL NINJA BE LIKE?

You've got thirty seconds to come up with eight great comparisons!

Fast as a . . . *cheetah*

Brave as a . . .

Dangerous as a . . .

Skillful as a . . .

Agile as a . . .

Quiet as a . . .

Sneaky as a . . .

Flexible as a . . .

Sharp as a . . .

YOU ARE MAKING
A NINJA
MOVIE!

MY MOVIE IS ABOUT . . .

HAPPY ENDING . . .

CLIFFHANGER ENDING . . .

Design a supercool
NINJA MOTORCYCLE

FINISH THE COMIC!

Continue the story here, or make up
a new comic.

POSTCARD

You're visiting Ninjago's realms. Write a postcard to a friend.

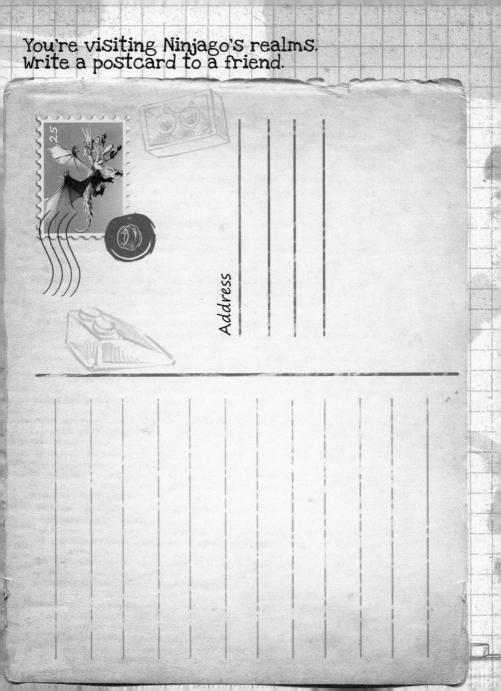

Address

CAN YOU READ
BACKWARD?

???

A gnol, gnol emit oga eht tsrif retsaM fo uztijnipS degrof ruof snopaew dna desu meht ot etaerc eht dlrow fo ogajniN.

Now write your own secret message:

Then write it backward here:

CREATE YOUR OWN

NINJA CODE OF LAWS

I would never: _____

_____

_____

_____

I will always guard: _____

_____

_____

_____

I promise: _____

_____

_____

_____

I would do anything to: _____

_____

_____

_____

I will always be ready to: _____

_____

_____

忍者

廻転

SPICE UP MASTER WU'S
WARDROBE!

Design new outfits for him.

PAJAMAS

CLOWN

FOR A DISCO PARTY

FOOTBALL FAN

APPLICATION

Your ninja nickname:

The element you control:
Your ninja color:
Your weapon of choice:
Name of a Spinjitzu move you've created?

Height: Weight:

How many hours do you sleep a day?
What kind of healthy food do you eat?

What do you practice?

What special talent do you have?

Date:

THE MAGNIFICENT MASTER

Draw yourself as **an Elemental Master** in action.

WHAT A HUGE HOUSE! WHY NOT MAKE IT NINJA HEADQUARTERS?

Draw the things the ninja would need in each room.

YOUR FAVORITE NINJA JOKES AND SAYINGS

What's the best thing about being a ninja?

Listening to jokes about ninja.

DESIGN YOUR OWN
TRAINING DUMMY

What would it look like after training?

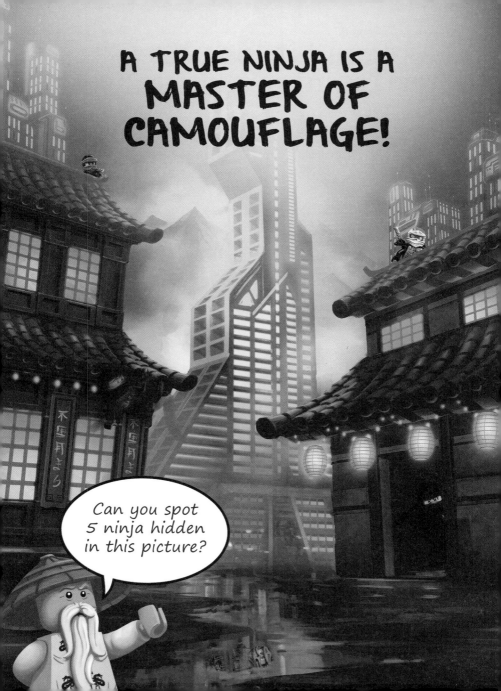

Draw the ninja hiding on this page!

A ninja can hide even on an empty page!

DESIGN YOUR OWN
SUPER WEAPON!

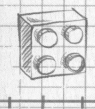

$17\frac{1}{2}$

MAKE YOUR OWN
GRAFFITI

NINJA'S SECRETS

Real ninja never give away their secrets.

Especially when the secret is really important!

93

Write a list of your deepest secrets

In each word swap the first letter with the last one. KOMEWORH SI GNIERESTINI OT EM.

. . . or replace letters with
numbers: A-1, B-2, C-3, D-4, etc.

CHOOSE YOUR TRAINING OPTION

PATH OF A DRAGON:

- flapping your arms as if you're about to take off
- swinging your leg around as if it were a dragon's tail
- practicing a menacing dragon expression in the mirror

SAMURAI'S WALK:

- cleaning your room without complaining
- developing your own samurai battle cry
- practicing a bold samurai swagger to your own theme music

NINDROID'S UPGRADE:

- doing laps around your computer
- reading a book backward
- playing your favorite computer game blindfolded

YOUR TRAINING OPTION:

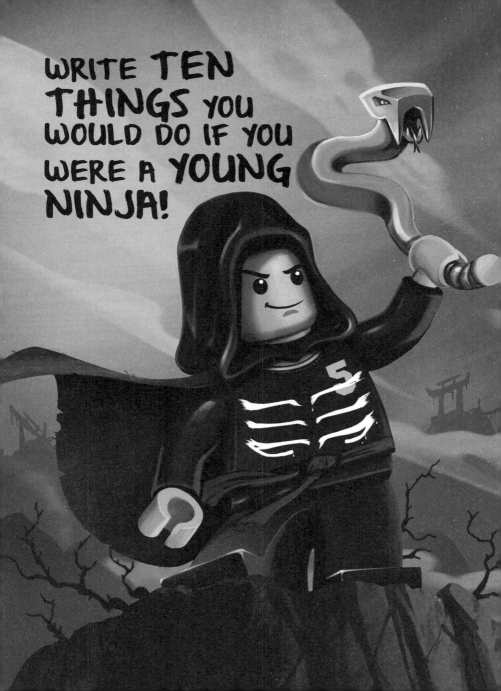

WRITE TEN THINGS YOU WOULD DO IF YOU WERE A YOUNG NINJA!

1. I would look for other ninja in the neighborhood.

2. I would form a super awesome team.

3.

4.

5.

6.

7.

8.

9.

10.

How do you act when you're angry?

I lose . . .

I shout . . .

What do you do to cool off?

I go . . .

I play . . .

Ha! That's so scary, it ALMOST gives me goose bumps.

THE NINJA KNOW HOW POWERFUL A **DRAGON** IS

what would your dragon look like?
Draw and describe it.

WHAT IS THE STRANGEST DREAM OR NIGHTMARE YOU'VE EVER HAD?

ALL NINJA HAVE THEIR OWN SIGNATURES!

Jay

Lloyd Nya

Kai

Wu

Cole

Have you got your own?

NOW ASK YOUR FRIENDS TO WRITE THEIR

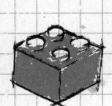

AUTOGRAPHS

HERE!

THE NINJA LOVE TO PLAY **GAMES**

List some of your favorite games below.

Let's play!!!

EACH NINJA HAS THEIR OWN SIGN

Draw a sign that represents you

HYPNOSIS
Don't stare at the spiral too long!

How can the ninja defend themselves from hypnosis?

Turning a mirror on the enemy is a good idea.

Master Wu loves his
AIRSHIP!
What does your ninja team's air fortress look like?

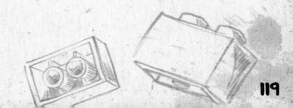

What would your mech look like? **Draw it**, and then write what it can do.

Try to build it with LEGO bricks, too!

NINJA TRAIN TO **PERFECTION** EVERY DAY . . .

. . . ALMOST

what are you good at?

what else would you like to be good at?

NOTEBOOK

Use these notebook pages to write or sketch anything you like. You can even draw the ninja!

NOTEBOOK

NOTEBOOK

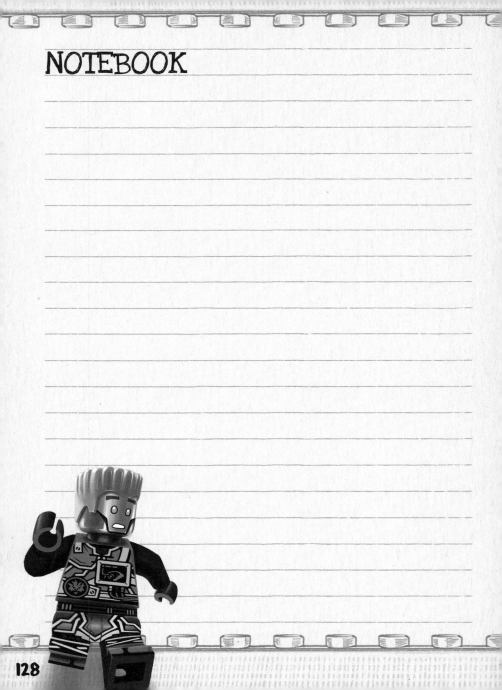

NOTEBOOK

NOTEBOOK

NOTEBOOK

NOTEBOOK

NOTEBOOK

NOTEBOOK

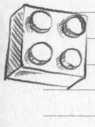

WHICH SPINJITZU MASTER
WOULD YOU MOST LIKE TO BE?

Kai: Nothing is impossible for you! You love action and know no fear. Your energy and determination give others the will to fight. You're a vital part of the team!

Nya: You get along with everyone and can find a solution to every problem. You like to keep busy, and the team can always count on you to get them out of trouble.

Zane: You spend a lot of time thinking and analysing situations. You have a cool-headed approach and don't let your emotions get the best of you. You see more than others, which makes you a great member of every ninja team.

Jay: "Fast" should be your middle name. You tend to think on your feet and act with lightning-fast speed. You like telling jokes, and although your friends don't always get them, it's always fun when you're around.

Lloyd: You are serious, decisive, and mature. When you start something, you finish it. You take learning seriously, knowing that there is no success without training. You'd make a great leader!

Cole: You're as calm as a rock and as hard as . . . a rock. Despite the fact that you like adrenaline, your friends feel safe around you. Your strength and inner balance keep the ninja team grounded.

HOW TO BUILD LLOYD